ISBN 1 85854 242 1
© Brimax Books 1995. All rights reserved.
Published by Brimax Books, Newmarket, England CB8 7AU 1995.
Printed in Dubai.

THE ODYSSEY

Adapted by John Escott

Illustrated by Roger Payne

BRIMAX · NEWMARKET · ENGLAND

Introduction

In this edition of The Odyssey young children will be
able to read about the adventures of the Greek hero,
Odysseus, as he sails home to Ithaca after the Trojan
war. It proves to be a perilous journey, full of mortal
danger. Before Odysseus reaches Ithaca he has to face
the terrors of Polyphemus the cyclops, the monster
Scylla and the vast whirlpool Charybdis. Once home,
Odysseus is not immediately recognised and rivals are
trying to steal his palace and his wife, Penelope.
A mighty contest must be fought before Odysseus can
gain his rightful place as King of Ithaca.

Contents

The Trojan Horse

Odysseus, warrior and Greek King of Ithaca, looked across the wide plain towards the city of Troy. It stood on a hill, surrounded by thick, high walls which for ten years had kept out the Greek soldiers.

Inside those walls was Helen, the beautiful young wife of Menelaus, the Greek King of Sparta. Paris, the son of the Trojan King Priam, had enchanted and enticed the lovely Helen away from the Greek King's palace to Troy, and when Menelaus discovered this he was furious. He and the other Kings of the Greek empire – including Odysseus – took ships and soldiers to attack Troy and bring back Menelaus' beloved wife, but so far the Trojan defences had proved too strong and Helen was still a captive.

The time had come, Odysseus decided, for a new, more cunning tactic.

Athene, Goddess of Wisdom and protector of Odysseus throughout the battles, planted a bold and artful idea into his head.

"Send me Epeius, the carpenter," said Odysseus, smiling to himself.

Several days later, the Trojans looked out from the city and were amazed to see that the Greek soldiers had gone, and that their ships were sailing away into the distance. And on the shore stood the strangest sight they had ever seen – a huge wooden horse!

Helen was dismayed to see the Greeks sailing away, for she longed to be back with Menelaus. But King Priam and his daughter, Cassandra, simply stared in wonderment at the enormous wooden animal.

"It must be a gift!" laughed Priam. "The Greeks have left us a parting gift in recognition of their defeat!"

Cassandra, blessed with the power of fore-telling the future, was not fooled. "It's a trick," she cried. "It's full of Greek soldiers!" But nobody listened to Cassandra, for although the God Apollo had given her the power to see into the future, he had also made certain that nobody believed her. It was a punishment for making him angry.

Just then, a single Greek soldier was dis-covered near the city and was quickly arrested and brought before King Priam.

"Who are you?" the King asked him.

"Sinon, a relative of Odysseus," replied the man. "We had a quarrel and I stayed behind when the others sailed away."

"Tell me," said the King, "what is the purpose of this wooden horse?"

"It's a tribute to the Goddess Athene," said Sinon.

Not wishing to offend the Goddess, King Priam instructed his men to bring the horse inside the walls of the city, where the people stood and stared at it.

That evening, the Trojans celebrated with a great feast and it was late into the night before the last man fell into a drunken sleep.

This was the moment Sinon had been waiting for. He hurried to the wooden horse and climbed up one of the legs. On the underside of the horse was a concealed door, and Sinon opened it. A ladder dropped down and, one after another, Greek soldiers descended swiftly and silently, each man armed with spear and sword.

Sinon lit a beacon – the signal for the Greeks to attack! They rushed into the houses and killed the Trojans as they slept. Out at sea, the Greek ships were waiting, and when they saw the flames from the beacon, they sailed back to Troy. Thousands of soldiers swarmed across the plain. They burned the city, killing every man and taking the young women away to be slaves.

King Priam and his sons were killed in the royal palace, and Menelaus and Helen were joyfully reunited. After this, the Greeks took the treasures from the burning city and, leaving it to fall in flames and smoke behind them, set sail for home.

The Cicones and the Lotus Eaters

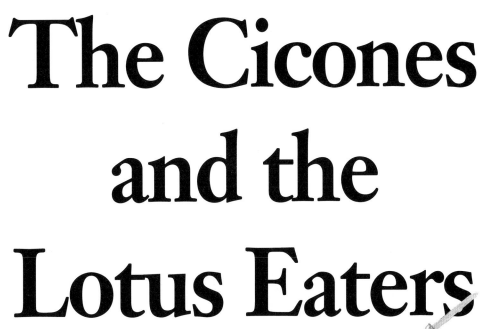

H ome for Odysseus was the rocky little island of Ithaca, which lay off the mainland of Greece. And after ten weary years of battles, he could not wait to get there.

After a few days sailing and rowing, Odysseus came to the land of the Cicones. These people had sent men to help the Trojans fight against the Greeks, so Odysseus had no hesitation in making a swift and deadly raid to get fresh supplies of food and drink for his journey.

They attacked Ismarus, the main town, and the people were taken by surprise. Their homes were robbed and their men killed, and only a handful managed to escape.

Back at the beach, Odysseus and his men divided up the spoils between the twelve ships, each man taking his share.

"We must leave at once," Odysseus told his men, but they insisted on building fires on the beach and killing some of the Cicones' cattle for a feast. Much wine was drunk and they slept heavily afterwards.

Meanwhile, the few Cicones who had escaped fetched help from more of their countrymen and came back to take their revenge. At dawn the following day, Odysseus and his men awoke to the sound of chariot wheels as the Cicones swept down on to the Greek camp. It was the turn of Odysseus and his men to be the victims of a surprise attack.

They fought with their backs to the sea until finally there was nothing for it but to flee to their ships.

But it had been a costly venture. Six men from each of the twelve ships had lost their lives.

After only a few days, the ships ran into a gale and were blown miles off their course. It was a further nine days when they saw the land of the Lotus Eaters, where the people ate nothing but the juicy fruit of the Lotus plant and dreamed their time away.

Odysseus and his men put in to shore and three men were sent to explore and report back. The men set out to discover what they could, but before they had gone far they met with a group of the Lotus Eaters.

The Greeks were immediately made welcome and given some Lotus fruit to eat. As soon as they tasted it, they lost all desire to return to their friends and were overwhelmed by a strange and beautiful feeling of peace and happiness.

When his men did not return, Odysseus went in search of them. He was very angry when he found them, and he and his followers dragged them back to the ships. The men wailed and protested. They did not want to go to sea, they wanted to stay with the Lotus Eaters. But Odysseus knew that he would lose all of his men if he didn't get them away quickly.

'Once the rest of them taste that fruit, I will never get them home,' he thought.

And with all speed, he made them row away.

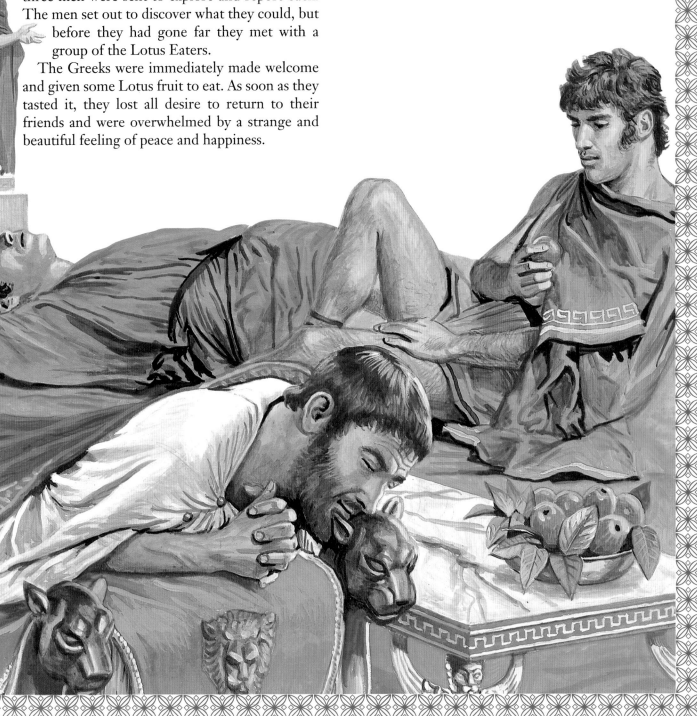

The Cyclops

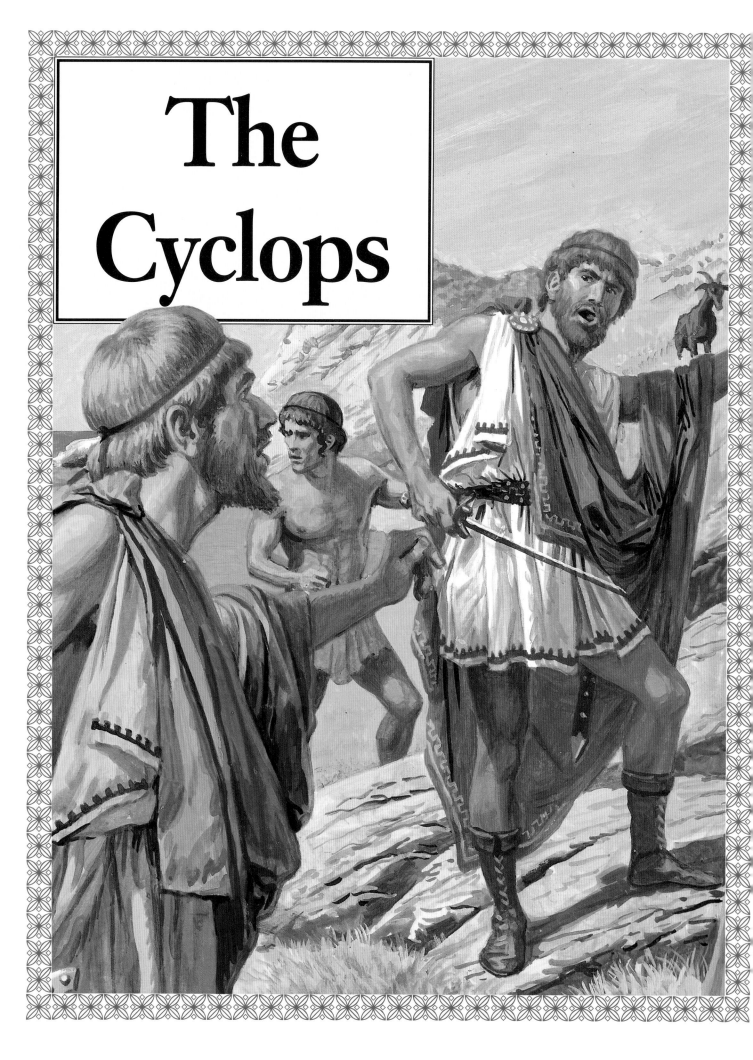

A thick mist surrounded Odysseus' ships and he peered into the darkness as his men rowed. After some time, their ships ran aground on a beach. Although they did not know it, they were in the country of the Cyclops – savage giants who lived in caves in the hills.

Odysseus and his men slept. When they awoke, the mist had lifted and they found themselves on a small wooded island. They were alone, except for the wild goats grazing nearby. Across the water was the mainland with its rocky hills, and the scattered herds of goats and sheep.

"Tomorrow, I'll take twelve men and go there to explore," said Odysseus.

This he did, taking some wine as a gift for anyone they might meet. Once ashore, Odysseus and his men climbed up the rocky hills to the mouth of a huge cave. They found lambs and goats in a pen and, further inside the cave, great pails of milk and huge baskets filled with cheeses.

The men wanted to return to their ships, but Odysseus was curious.

"We'll wait," he said. "I want to see who lives here."

It was late evening when they heard heavy footsteps approaching. Suddenly, a huge shape filled the mouth of the cave and Odysseus and his men fled to the darkest corners to hide.

The creature rolled a massive rock across the cave entrance, then threw down branches from a tree to start a fire. As the flames lit up the cave, Odysseus and his men caught sight of the giant for the first time – and they gasped in horror! Not only was he the biggest creature they had ever seen, but he had one huge and terrifying eye in the centre of his forehead.

The Cyclops saw Odysseus and his friends crouching in the shadows.

"Who are you?" he roared.

Bravely, Odysseus stepped forward. "We're Greeks on our way home after the war with Troy," he said. "The winds blew us to your land."

"I am Polyphemus," the Cyclops said. "Where is your ship?"

Odysseus guessed that the Cyclops meant to

destroy his ships and the men guarding them so he said, "Our ship was wrecked. These twelve men and I are the only survivors who managed to swim ashore."

The Cyclops seized two of the men and smashed their bodies on the floor of the cave, then proceeded to eat them for his supper. After this, he drank several pails of milk before lying down beside the fire to sleep.

Odysseus could have killed the Cyclops with his sword, but this would have left them trapped inside the cave, so he and his men waited to see what the next day would bring.

The Cyclops woke at dawn, snatched two more of Odysseus' men and ate them for his breakfast. He pushed aside the huge rock and drove out his sheep and goats before rolling it back again and walking off to the hills.

Odysseus and the eight remaining men tried to think of a way to outwit the giant. Suddenly, Odysseus saw a thick wooden staff at the back of the cave and had an idea. He used his sword to cut off a piece of wood about the height of a man, then sharpened the end and pushed it into the fire to harden the point before hiding it at the back of the cave.

That evening, the giant snatched two more men for his supper and, while he was eating them, Odysseus took out the wine they had brought with them. "Try some of this," he said to the giant.

The Cyclops held out a wooden bowl which Odysseus filled, then he drank it in one gulp. "Give me more," he said, holding out the bowl again. And once more the giant drank it in one swallow.

As Odysseus filled the bowl again, he said, "My name is No Man."

"No Man, is it?" said the giant. "Well, No Man, I shall eat every man here, but I will leave you until last. That's a promise."

But after two more drinks, the giant fell asleep.

"Fetch me the stake," said Odysseus. "Quickly!"

The wooden stake was held in the fire until it was red-hot, then Odysseus and four men plunged it deep into the giant's eye.

The Cyclops gave a scream of pain, pulled the stake out of his eye and stumbled blindly round the cave trying to catch Odysseus and his men. His shouts woke the other Cyclops in nearby caves.

"What is it, Polyphemus?" they cried. "Why do you wake us?"

"No Man is trying to kill me!" roared the giant.

The other Cyclops were annoyed. "If no man is trying to kill you, why wake us? You must be losing your mind! Leave us to our sleep."

The giant felt his way across to the entrance of the cave and rolled the stone away. He sat down in the doorway.

"You will not escape," he told Odysseus.

But Odysseus and his men were too clever for the giant. They tied together eighteen of the sheep in threes, then one man climbed under each middle sheep and held on. Odysseus took the biggest ram and held on underneath the shaggy wool, completely hidden.

It was dawn now and the sheep were anxious to be grazing on the hills. They moved towards the entrance and Polyphemus felt the back of each one before allowing them to pass out of the cave.

Odysseus was last. The giant put out a hand and immediately recognised his biggest ram. "Why aren't you leading the flock today?" he asked. "Are you sad because your master has lost his eye? If you could speak, you'd tell me where No Man is hiding, then I could kill him."

The ram was allowed to pass and, underneath it, Odysseus breathed more easily. Once outside, he and his men quickly ran back to their boat and rowed towards the small island. When they were a safe distance away, Odysseus shouted back at the mainland, "You have been punished, Polyphemus! You should not kill innocent strangers!"

The Cyclops heard him and ran from the cave. He picked up a big rock and threw it in the direction of Odysseus' voice. It fell close to the ship, making a huge wave which almost swamped it.

Odysseus taunted the giant again. "If anyone

asks how you lost your eye," he shouted, "tell them it was not No Man who tricked you but Odysseus, King of Ithaca."

"You will suffer for this!" shouted the Cyclops. "Poseidon, God of the Sea, is my father and will take revenge on you, Odysseus!"

But Odysseus and his friends did not hear. They were already back on the little island. And after a very short time, Odysseus and all his remaining men set sail in their ships.

The Ship of
Fools and the
Laestrygonians

A few days after their escape from the Cyclops, they saw the steep cliffs of a strange island. It was the floating island home of Aeolus, Ruler of the Winds, who lived there with his wife and twelve children – six sons and six daughters. His palace was surrounded by a wall of bronze which glittered in the sunlight.

Odysseus decided to call and ask Aeolus for help.

They were made most welcome, and Aeolus asked many questions about the battles at Troy. They ate and drank and talked for several days, but at last it was time for Odysseus to leave and he asked the Ruler of the Winds to use his powers to help them.

Aeolus gave him a leather bag, tied with a silver thread.

"Do not open this until you are safely home," he told Odysseus. "Inside are all the winds except one – the westward one, which you will need for a swift and safe voyage."

Odysseus kept the leather bag close to him and told no one about its secrets. As the men rowed and the favourable west wind filled the sails, their ships sped across the ocean, drawing ever closer to Ithaca.

Ten days later, a great cheer went up from Odysseus and his men. There ahead of them was the coastline of Ithaca, only a few hours away!

At last, Odysseus felt able to relax, but as he slept his men began to talk among themselves. "Odysseus will be a rich man with all the treasures from the Trojan war," one said.

"Aeolus gave him treasure before we left," said another. "Odysseus keeps it hidden in that leather bag. Why don't we see what it is?"

"It's only right that we should share in any treasure," the men said to each other. "We've faced the same dangers as Odysseus."

The bag was opened – and the winds burst out with a great roar! They filled the sky and whipped up the waves until the ships began to toss and roll in the angry sea. Odysseus woke up.

"What have you done?" he cried. And then he saw the empty leather bag. "Fools! I have a ship of fools!"

The winds blew them back into the open sea, and Ithaca disappeared. For Odysseus, it was almost too much to bear. He had been so close to home, but now he was heading straight back to the island of Aeolus!

Aeolus was astonished to see them. "What happened?" he asked.

Odysseus explained. "My men opened the bag of winds while I was asleep," he said. "Please, give me your help again!"

Aeolus was angry. "Go immediately, and without my help! You're clearly the unluckiest of all men and we don't want your bad luck here."

So Odysseus and his ships were forced to leave.

For six days they fought the gales until, on the seventh, they saw land. It was Laestrygonia, the home of giants, although they did not know this.

They found a safe harbour and eleven of Odysseus' ships dropped anchor in the bay whilst Odysseus tied his own ship to a rock on a headland. He sent three men ashore to look around the island.

Only two of the men returned, and they were running for their lives!

"We met a young woman," gasped one. "She was a giant, and she took us to her village. Her father was Antiphates, Chief of the Laestry-gonians, but it was her mother whom we met first – a woman as tall as a mountain! She called

her husband and he seized our companion and said that he was going to eat him for his supper!"

"We ran away before he could catch us too," said the other man.

Suddenly, as the two men finished their ghastly story, the ships in the harbour were bombarded with enormous rocks. These crashed down with deadly accuracy, sinking ship after ship until the sea was dotted with drowning men. Odysseus looked up and saw the terrifying giants who were throwing the rocks from the cliff above.

A handful of Odysseus' men swam towards his ship, the only one afloat now, but the giants used their spears to kill them. There were ropes attached to the spears, and the giants hauled in their catch like fish.

There was nothing Odysseus could do to save the rest of his ships so he cut his own free from the headland and shouted: "Row for your lives!"

Somehow, they escaped from that terrible island. But of the twelve ships that had sailed from Troy, now only one was left.

Circe

Odysseus and his men sailed on with heavy hearts after the loss of their friends. Many days and nights later they found another island and, weary from their journey, struggled ashore to rest. For two days they did nothing but sleep and grieve for their dead companions. But then Odysseus decided to explore part of the island on his own.

He climbed a rocky hill, the morning sun warm on his back, and when he reached the top he looked across the top of a forest and saw blue smoke rising from a clearing amongst the trees.

A stag moved out of the trees and took a drink from a stream below the place where Odysseus was standing. Swiftly and silently, Odysseus ran down the hill, raised his spear and threw it – and it found its target!

Odysseus cut the supple branches from a young willow tree and used them as rope to tie the dead stag's feet. Then he heaved the animal across his shoulders and walked back to the shore.

He woke his men with a shout. "Food!" he cried.

A fire was lit, and the venison roasted over it. All day, Odysseus and his men feasted, until the sun finally slipped below the horizon.

Next day, Odysseus told his men about the smoke he had seen. He divided them into two groups – one under his own command, the other with Eurylochus as their leader. They drew lots to decide who should stay with the ship and who should explore, and it was Eurylochus who went out with his twenty-two men.

When they reached the clearing in the forest, they found a beautiful palace. But as they moved out of the trees, one man shouted a warning.

"Wolves!" he cried. "Lions!"

The others turned to see a pack of wolves, with lions beside them. In moments, Eurylochus and his men were surrounded. But the animals did not attack. The lions purred like cats and the wolves wagged their tails.

"What strange creatures are these?" said Eurylochus.

A voice came from inside the palace. It was a woman, singing. Suddenly, the door opened and there she stood, young and beautiful.

"Come in," she said. "I am Circe and this is my home."

Spellbound, the men followed her inside. All except Eurylochus who ran and hid in the trees because he did not trust her.

He was right to be suspicious. Circe led the others into her palace and gave them food and wine, and after the men had finished eating and drinking they could not remember who they were or where they had come from. Then, with a wave of her magic wand, Circe turned them into pigs and drove them out into the courtyard and into a sty.

The men had been allowed to keep their own minds, and wept bitterly at their fate as Circe threw down a handful of acorns for them to eat.

Eurylochus ran back to Odysseus to tell him what had happened.

"Come back to this palace with me," said Odysseus.

But Eurylochus was afraid. "Let's get away while we can," he said.

"No, I can't leave my men without trying to help them," said Odysseus, and he went off alone.

On the way to the palace, Odysseus met a young shepherd, who was really Hermes, Messenger of the Gods and son of Zeus, in disguise.

"Greetings, Odysseus," said Hermes. "Have you come to free your friends from the witch, Circe? Then I can help you." He stooped to the ground and picked a small plant with a black root and a white flower. "Take this with the wine or food she gives you, and when she touches you with her wand, draw your sword and pretend you mean to kill her. Make her promise not to use her magic on you."

And in the next moment, Hermes was gone.

Circe greeted Odysseus with a smile and invited him in. She gave him poisoned wine in a golden cup and touched him with her magic wand, but the little plant protected him. Odysseus drew his sword.

Circe gave a cry of terror. "Who are you? Can you – can you be Odysseus, the Greek warrior who is famous for his skill and cunning? Hermes told me that you would come some day."

Odysseus made her promise not to harm him, and Circe removed the spell from his men so that they were no longer pigs but men again.

"Fetch your other men from the beach," Circe told Odysseus. "They, too, can come and eat with us. We will all feast happily together."

They stayed with Circe for a year, resting and enjoying the luxury of her palace. But the time came when each man knew they must continue their journey home to Ithaca.

"You must go to the land of Hades," Circe told Odysseus, "the God who rules the spirits of the dead. The spirit of Teiresias, the blind prophet, is waiting to speak with you. You must not continue your journey until you have seen him."

Odysseus was frightened. "Hades! Only dead men go here!" he cried.

"Don't be afraid," said Circe. "The wind will take you there. Walk through the forest of dead trees until you come to a rock, where two rivers join together and flow into a third. There you must sacrifice a ram and a black ewe and call up the spirit of Teiresias. He will tell you all you need to know."

Early the next day, Odysseus called his men together. But before they could sail, Elpenor, the youngest crew member, died in a tragic accident. He fell to his death from an upstairs window.

This was bad enough, but when the men heard they had to go to Hades before they could continue their journey, they went white with fear.

Hades

dark place. A threatening place, where mists shrouded everything and the eerie silence was broken only by the sound of Odysseus' ship touching the shingled shore. This was Hades.

"Wait for me," Odysseus told his frightened men. And he took the ram and the black ewe and set off into the forest of dead trees, looking for the rock where the two rivers joined and flowed into the third.

He found it without any trouble, and quickly dug a pit and sacrificed the two animals. Immediately, ghosts appeared and hovered around him – hundreds of them, young and old, men and women.

Odysseus recognised one of the faces. It was Elpenor, the young crew member who had died at Circe's palace!

"My noble leader," said Elpenor, "my body remains on Circe's island, not yet buried. I beg you to return and burn it, then to take the oar I rowed with in our ship and lay it on my grave."

With tears in his eyes, Odysseus promised to do this, and the young crewman drifted away.

Immediately, Teiresias appeared and spoke to Odysseus.

"You wish to know your fate, Odysseus," he said. "Well, I can promise you a long and difficult journey, for you angered Poseidon, God of the Sea, by blinding his son, Polyphemus. You must be careful not to anger Hyperion, the Sun God, when you pass the island where he keeps his cattle. Do not harm a single animal if you want to avoid his rage. And when you reach home, you

will find evil men plotting to steal your wife and your kingdom from you. But Odysseus, I can at least promise you a peaceful death in your old age."

Odysseus watched fearfully as Teiresias disappeared and another figure took his place. To Odysseus' astonishment, it was Anticleia, his own mother! He had not known she was dead!

"Mother, why are you here?" cried Odysseus.

"I died of a broken heart waiting for your return, my son," she said.

"And my father, Laertes?"

"He is alive, but he too has a broken heart and no longer lives in the palace. He spends his days working in the fields, like a common labourer, waiting for your return. Your wife, Penelope, is equally unhappy, wondering if she will ever see you again."

Odysseus reached out to hold his mother, but there was nothing for his arms to hold. Her ghostly figure melted away before his eyes.

Odysseus spoke with some of the other spirits, among them Agamemnon, commander of all the Greeks at Troy.

"Did you not get home alive?" Odysseus asked him.

"Yes," he replied, "only to discover that my wife, Clytemnestra, had taken a lover, who killed me as I sat down to a welcoming feast! You have a good wife, Odysseus, but take care that my terrible fate doesn't await you, too."

There were other warriors who came to speak to Odysseus. Achilles, killed by an arrow at Troy. Ajax, who had killed himself from jealousy when Achilles' armour was given to Odysseus instead of him. He could not forgive Odysseus this.

Odysseus could stand this miserable place no longer, and fled.

The Sirens, Scylla and Charybdis

Odysseus and his men sailed for many days before they got back to Circe's island. Here, Odysseus did as Elpenor had asked, burning the young man's body and then taking the oar and laying it on his grave.

Odysseus and his men stayed one more night with Circe, and she took the opportunity to speak secretly to Odysseus.

"There are other dangers for you that Tieresias didn't mention," she said. "Close to these shores are the Sirens, who sing their songs to tempt passing sailors to stop. Their island is littered with the bones of men who were spellbound by those songs, and who died there. Be sure that you and your men do not hear them."

"What then?" asked Odysseus.

"After this, you will have a choice," said Circe. "You can pass by the Wandering Rocks, which are sometimes hidden and sometimes uncovered, making it seem as if they are always on the move. But I suggest you take the other route, between two islands. Look for the highest cliff, and the cave where the sea-monster, Scylla, lives. She has six hideous heads and barks and howls like a dog. With each head, she will eat one sailor from any ship that goes by. Beneath the other cliff is Charybdis' whirlpool which, three times a day, sucks down anything sailing in it, and three times a day she spouts it up like a fountain."

"So there is no safe route?" said Odysseus.

"No, but if you stay close to the high cliff, Scylla can only take six of your men," said Circe. "Better that than to lose your whole ship in Charybdis' whirlpool."

Next morning, Odysseus said goodbye to Circe, fearful for the future of himself and his men.

When Odysseus first saw the island of the

Sirens, he warned his men of the dangers and gave each of them wax to put in their ears so that they should not hear the creatures singing. He put no wax in his own ears but ordered his men to tie him to the mast so that he could not be tempted away.

The Sirens saw Odysseus' ship coming and began to sing their song. They had the bodies of huge birds but the heads of beautiful women with long, golden hair.

The magic of the song soon began to work on Odysseus and he struggled to free himself. But his men tied him tighter and they sailed safely past the bewitching creatures.

When the Sirens were out of sight and hearing, Odysseus' men untied him, just in time to see two more islands in the distance. There was a narrow stretch of water between them for Odysseus' ship to sail through. He could see the whirlpool on one side and the entrance to Scylla's cave in the cliffs on the other.

The men knew nothing of the six-headed Scylla and they steered the ship away from the whirlpool.

"Keep close to the other cliff," Odysseus told them, then put on his armour and took up his sword.

He meant to keep watch for Scylla, hoping to chop off one of her heads, but Charybdis blew out her foul breath and sprayed them with water, distracting Odysseus. In an instant, Scylla's six heads leapt out of the cave and snatched six of Odysseus' men! Odysseus heard their screams as the terrible monster ate them in the entrance to her cave.

It was all over in seconds.

Hyperion
and
Calypso

Odysseus saw the island of Hyperion as the sun began to set that evening. He remembered the warning of Teiresias, not to anger the Sun God or harm his herds of cattle, and he decided not to stop there. But his men were weary and persuaded him to drop anchor.

They went ashore, but Odysseus made them promise to keep away from Hyperion's sacred herds. They built fires and ate a meal, then fell asleep under the stars.

But during the night a breeze sprang up and, by morning, the wind was blowing wildly and waves were crashing on the shore. They could not risk sailing in such a gale and so they pulled their ship across the beach and into a cave for shelter.

The fierce storms continued day after day, week after week, and very soon there was nothing left to eat. They caught fish, but these were always tiny. They looked for sea creatures under the rocks or caught an occasional bird, but there was never enough for a meal. Soon, Odysseus and his men began to starve.

On the twentieth day, Odysseus fell asleep in the afternoon, weak from hunger. His men were discussing what to do next when some of Hyperion's cattle began to graze nearby.

"I will not die of hunger," announced Eurylochus, when he saw them. "If the Gods are angry and sink our ship, then we shall drown, but at least it will be a quick death. Let's kill the fattest cow."

The other men agreed and, whilst Odysseus slept, they slaughtered the biggest animal and roasted it over a fire. But the smell of the meat cooking woke Odysseus and he immediately guessed what they had done.

"You fools!" he cried.

But the men took no notice and ate the meat, even though it bellowed as if the cow were still alive.

The next day was calm and at last Odysseus was able to leave the island. But within the hour, thunder clouds massed in the sky above Odysseus' ship and a savage storm struck. The ship's mast snapped, killing a man as it fell, and all except Odysseus were thrown overboard where the sea swallowed them up.

The ship broke up and sank, and Odysseus grabbed at the broken mast and clung to it as the sea raged around him. He was tossed and thrown in every direction, and after nine days adrift, was washed ashore on the island of Ogygia, a wild paradise as beautiful as the nymph goddess, Calypso, who lived there.

Calypso lived in an enchanted cavern, waited on by maidservants who brought her ambrosia and nectar to eat and drink. That morning when Odysseus was washed ashore, Calypso was walking along the golden sand when she found him, half-drowned and his tunic in rags.

Calypso revived him with water from a spring, then helped him back to her cavern. There, over several days, she nursed him back to health and gave him a fresh tunic to wear. And as Odysseus grew strong again, Calypso fell in love with him.

"I can give you eternal youth and much happiness if you will only stay with me," she told him.

But Odysseus longed to see his wife, even though Calypso was more beautiful than any woman he had ever seen. "I want to go home," he said.

Calypso did not want to hear this. She had the power to free him but she would not. Instead, she made Odysseus a prisoner on her island paradise and kept him there for seven long years.

Each day, Odysseus sat on the shore and stared at the sea, thinking of his faraway home and wondering if he would ever see it again.

Athene, Goddess of Wisdom

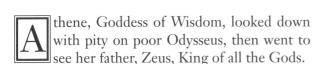thene, Goddess of Wisdom, looked down with pity on poor Odysseus, then went to see her father, Zeus, King of all the Gods.

"Odysseus has been unlucky. His ships are lost, his men are drowned, and now he is a prisoner on Calypso's island. Is it not time we helped him? He is, after all, a brave and clever man who deserves better."

"Odysseus' troubles are his punishment for blinding the Cyclops Polyphemus, son of Poseidon," answered Zeus. "You must talk to Poseidon."

"Please, father," said Athene, "send Hermes to tell Calypso to let Odysseus go. I will visit Telemachus, Odysseus' son, in Ithaca. He is almost twenty years old and must learn the ways of the world."

Zeus eventually agreed, for he enjoyed pleasing his daughter, and Athene went to Ithaca where she pretended to be Mentes, an old friend of Odysseus whom Telemachus had never seen.

Telemachus welcomed her warmly, as was the custom, and they sat down to eat in the palace. A man called Antinous who was an admirer of Penelope came to sit with them. He rudely demanded food and the best wine from a servant who hurried away to fetch it. Two more of Penelope's suitors joined him. They were Eurymachus and Amphinomus, and they ordered music to be played in the Great Hall of the palace.

As the music began, more than a hundred other unmarried princes from the island kingdoms arrived, helping themselves to food and wine.

Telemachus became angry. "They steal my father's food and wine, and they would steal his wife given the chance!"

"I am Mentes, a friend of your father," said Athene. "You are only young, I know, but you must get rid of these suitors and prove to the people of Ithaca that you are ready to take your father's place."

"How?" said Telemachus.

"First, call an assembly of lords, counsellors, noblemen and all the people and tell them what these men are doing. Then go and see Menelaus and Nestor, your father's old friends," said Athene. "Perhaps they have news of Odysseus. Also, the people will see how brave you are to make such a long and dangerous journey and respect you for it. Then they will treat you like a man, not a boy."

So the next day, Telemachus called an assembly of the people and spoke to them about the suitors and the torment these princes caused Penelope. "They steal my father's food and wine," said Telemachus, "and they are trying to steal his wife!"

One of the suitors, Antinous, was angry. "Your mother has played a game with us," he complained. "She said that when the cloak she was weaving for your grandfather, Laertes, was finished, she might marry one of us. But for three years she secretly undid each day's work so that the cloak would *never* be finished."

"This is because she wants you to leave her alone," said Telemachus. "And if you don't, then Zeus will punish you."

As he spoke, two eagles flew above the crowd and attacked each other. Their blood dropped on to the heads below. "It is a sign from Zeus!" cried the crowd. "Odysseus is alive and will come back!"

The assembly broke up and Telemachus spoke again with Antinous and Eurymachus. "I'm going to visit Nestor and Menelaus to see if they have news of Odysseus," he said. "If my father is dead,

then my mother will make her decision about marrying again. Until then, I want you and all the suitors to return to your homes."

"We'll only leave when we have an answer from Penelope," said Antinous. "And where will you get enough courage for such a journey? You are only a boy!"

"I am Odysseus' son and heir," Telemachus said proudly.

That night, Telemachus sailed with Athene at his side. He said nothing to Penelope, telling only his old nurse, Eurycleia, and swearing her to secrecy.

Athene was disguised as Mentor, an old friend of Odysseus, and the journey, which might well have been dangerous, was calm and without problems because of her presence. They reached Pylos, King Nestor's city, in two days and Telemachus and Mentor visited the old king's palace. A nervous Telemachus was presented to Nestor and asked for news of his father.

"I have news of some of the other Greek leaders who fought at Troy," said Nestor, "but none of your father. I'm sorry."

Telemachus thanked him anyway. "If my father does not return home soon, he will have no kingdom to return to," he said, "for there are men trying to steal it from him." And he told Nestor about the suitors.

"Then don't stay away too long," said Nestor, "but go and see King Menelaus before you return. I'll give you a chariot, and my son, Peisistratus, can go with you."

Next morning, the two young men set off for King Menelaus' palace, arriving there the evening of the following day. Menelaus was celebrating at the feast of his daughter's wedding, and he immediately invited the two young men to join his other guests.

Telemachus and Peisistratus were awed by the beautiful palace and its luxurious furnishings. Menelaus saw them admiring his home and smiled.

"Yes, I'm a wealthy man," he said. "But all my riches mean very little when I remember my friends who never came back from the wars. Heroes who are lost or dead. I remember especially my faithful friend Odysseus, who may be alive or dead, for all I know."

Telemachus turned away so that Menelaus should not see the tears in his eyes, but the King missed nothing and suddenly realised who his visitor was. But before anything more was said, a woman appeared at the King's side. Telemachus stared at her. She was the most stunningly beautiful woman he had ever seen, and she was looking directly at him.

"Do we know the name of our visitor, Menelaus?" she asked.

And then Telemachus realised that this was Helen, Menelaus' wife, who had been enticed to Troy by Paris, the Trojan Prince.

"I have not asked," said Menelaus. "I simply made him welcome."

"Do you not see the likeness, Menelaus?" said Helen. "There is no mistaking who this young man is. He is Telemachus, Odysseus' son."

"I just this moment realised it myself," said her husband. "So now he is doubly welcome!"

After the wedding feast was over, Telemachus asked again about his father.

"I have heard only one thing," said Menelaus. "Proteus, the Old Man of the Sea, said that he saw Odysseus on Calypso's island as he was passing it one day."

"Did he?" said Telemachus, excitedly. "Then perhaps he *is* alive and will come home soon!"

It was several days before the suitors discovered that Telemachus had sailed off to talk with King Nestor and King Menelaus.

"Who went with him?" Antinous asked the man who told them.

"Mentor was at the helm," said the man. "And yet I saw Mentor only yesterday, so how could it have been?"

The suitors schemed and plotted together. "Telemachus must not return," said Antinous. "We will secretly send a ship to attack him on the way back. No one will blame us, they will blame Zeus."

But they were overheard by Medon the Herald, who went quickly to Penelope to tell her. Penelope was puzzled. She knew nothing of her son's voyage.

"Bring Eurycleia to me," she said.

The old nurse came and eventually admitted the truth. Now Penelope was full of fear for her son. Was she to lose him, too? But that night Athene disguised herself as one of Penelope's friends and spoke to the Queen in a dream.

"Your son will be safe," Athene told her. "I will look after him."

And when Penelope woke in the morning, she was no longer afraid.

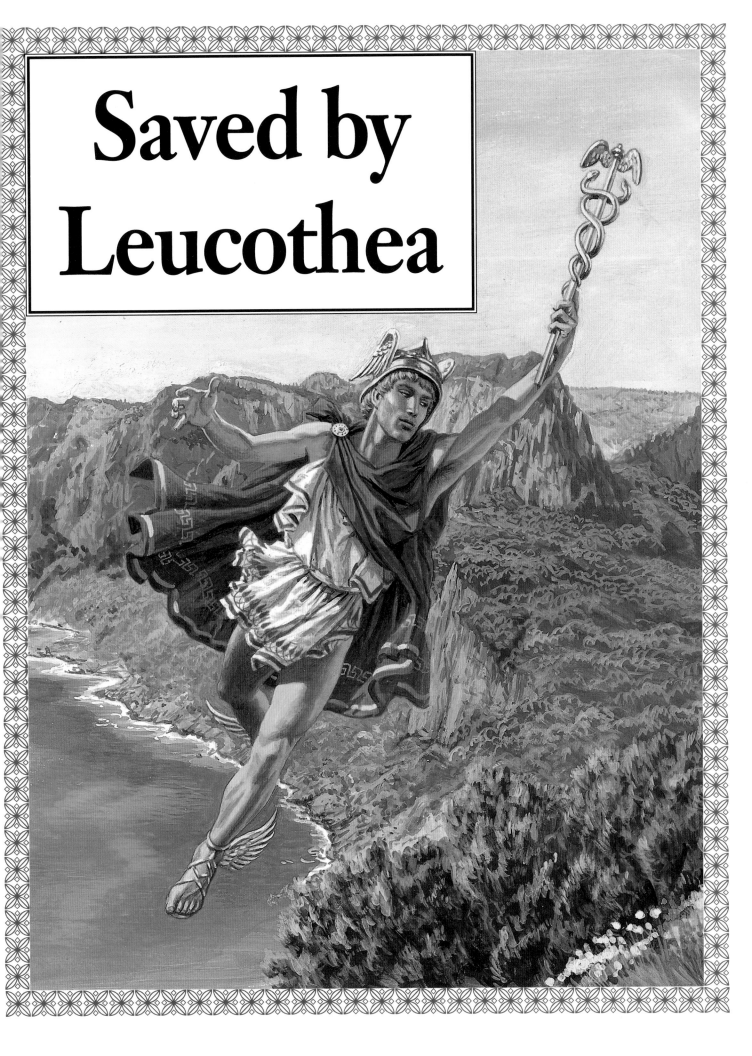

Saved by Leucothea

Zeus had done as his daughter asked and had sent Hermes, Messenger of the Gods, to Calypso to tell her to let Odysseus go. Hermes delivered the message.

"But I love Odysseus!" protested Calypso. "I have loved and cared for him since that day he was washed ashore. Give me more time, and perhaps he'll learn to love me, too. Besides, there is no ship on my island."

"Tell Odysseus to build a raft," said Hermes. "Now, do as Zeus commands and set Odysseus free."

After Hermes had gone, Calypso went to find Odysseus. He was sitting alone on the shore, staring unhappily out to sea.

"The time has come for you to leave," said Calypso.

Odysseus immediately brightened, but then frowned as he remembered something. "I have no ship," he said. "How can I sail anywhere?"

"I'll give you an axe to cut down some trees and build a raft," said Calypso. "And I'll give you warm clothing and food for the journey, and a kindly wind to carry you swiftly home."

"A raft?" said Odysseus. "How can a little raft survive on the open sea? It's a trick."

"Odysseus, I love you," said Calypso. "I swear before the Gods that I would not harm you."

At last, Odysseus cried out with joy at the thought of going home.

Calypso smiled sadly. "Are you so impatient to leave me?" she said. "Am I not more beautiful than your wife?"

"You are," said Odysseus, "but my only wish is to spend the rest of my life with Penelope."

For the next few days, he worked hard building his raft until it was ready to sail. Then Calypso gave him food, wine and warm clothing for the journey, and waved from the shore as he sailed away.

The calm and gentle wind stayed with him for seventeen days and nights, and on the eighteenth

day he saw land. He was so excited that at first he did not notice the wind change and the clouds begin to darken.

Poseidon had seen him and remembered the Cyclops Polyphemus, his son, whom Odysseus had blinded. Now was the time for Poseidon's revenge. He conjured up the most terrible storm so that Odysseus' little raft was tossed on the white-topped waves, and thrown about in the boiling sea. Odysseus managed to hold on for a time, but eventually he slipped overboard as the mast snapped in two and the sail blew away.

The warm clothes which Calypso had given Odysseus were heavy in the water and pulled him under. He forced his way up again, gasped for air, then swam to what was left of his raft. Clutching desperately to it, he was at the mercy of the waves, expecting to die as soon as the next one took him under again.

Suddenly, a strange figure came up out of the sea. It was Leucothea, the sea-nymph. "I'll save you!" she called out to Odysseus. She threw him her veil. "Take off your clothes so that they don't pull you down again, and tie this round your waist. It has magic powers. Then swim towards the coast that you can see in front of you. When you're safely ashore, throw the veil back into the sea."

And then she was gone.

Odysseus stripped off his clothes and tied the veil around his waist, then he stopped. Was this another trick of the Gods? Would he drown long before he reached land? But a huge wave swept over him and smashed the raft to pieces, and Odysseus had no choice but to swim for the coast.

For two days and two nights he swam until, exhausted but staying afloat because of the magic

veil, he saw the sharp rocks and fierce waves battering the cliffs ahead of him.

'I'll be torn to pieces if I try to go ashore there,' he thought.

He saw a rock and clung to it, waiting for a huge wave to roll back and sweep him out to sea again. When this happened, he battled against incoming waves until he found the mouth of a river which ran into the sea. Odysseus swam up the river until he felt the riverbed beneath his feet. Then he pulled off the veil and threw it back into the water before dragging himself to the river's edge and collapsing on the ground. Tired though he was, he managed to pull himself across to some bushes and, after covering himself with dead leaves, fell asleep, unaware that he was on the enchanted island of the Phaeacians.

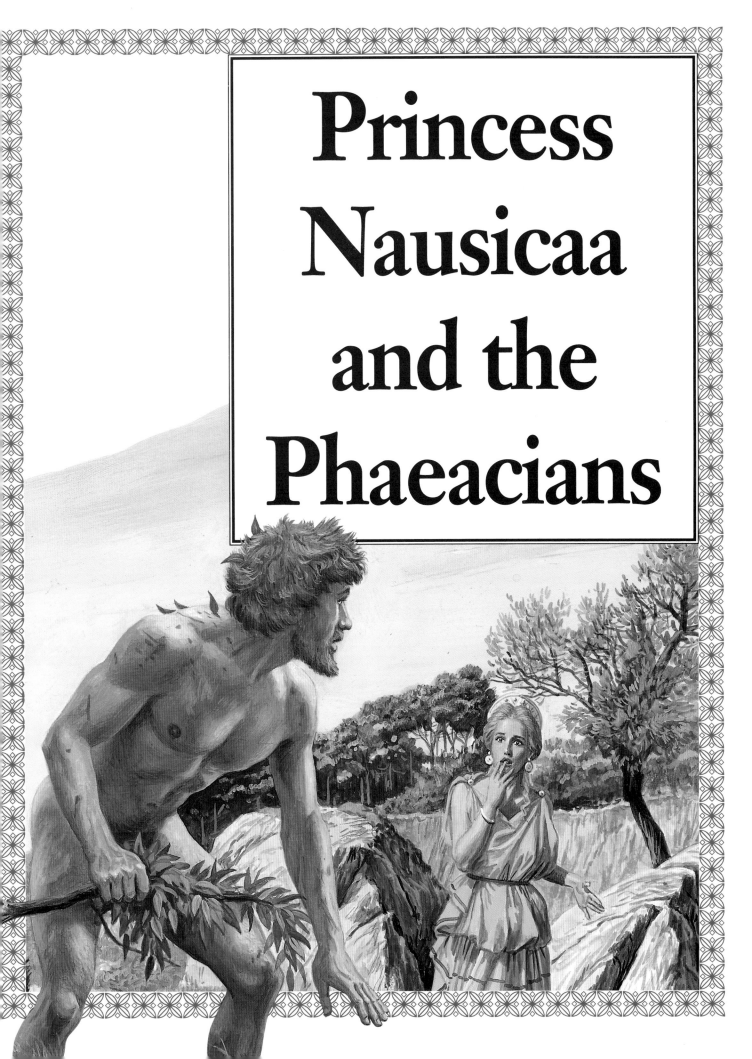

Princess Nausicaa and the Phaeacians

nother person on that island was also sleeping, and she was having a strange dream. It was Princess Nausicaa, the unmarried daughter of King Alcinous. In her dream, the princess was speaking with an old friend (although the 'old friend' was Athene, in disguise once again).

"Do not be lazy, Nausicaa," the friend was saying. "Go down to the river and wash your clothes, for some day you will be a bride and you and your family will need clean garments."

Nausicaa awoke and remembered her dream.

'How odd,' she thought. But she loaded a wagon with all her clothes, and the clothes of her brothers, and took them to the riverbank to wash. Nausicaa drove the wagon while her maidservants walked behind.

It was a beautiful warm morning and the sun sparkled on the river. They washed every garment and laid them out to dry in the hot sun. Then Nausicaa and her maidservants took off their clothes and bathed in the river themselves. Afterwards, they dried themselves, put on their clothes and began to play with a ball. They laughed and sang as they played, and the ball was thrown from one to the other until Nausicaa accidentally threw it into the river. It landed with a splash and floated away.

The noise of their laughter and singing had woken Odysseus from his long sleep. He looked out from behind the bushes and saw the girls playing together. Taking a branch to cover his nakedness, Odysseus stepped out. He was scratched and bruised and covered in sea-salt. The maidservants were frightened by the strange figure and ran away, but Nausicaa did not move.

Odysseus saw how beautiful she was and moved closer to her.

"Are you a Goddess?" he asked.

She smiled. "No, I am Nausicaa, and my father is King Alcinous. You are in the land of the Phaeacians. Let me help you."

She bathed his wounds and Odysseus washed the sea-salt from his body in the river. After this, Nausicaa gave him a warm red tunic to wear.

'How handsome he looks now,' she thought. 'Perhaps he will stay and make Phaeacia his home. He would make a perfect husband.'

The maidservants came back and they gave him some of the food and wine they had brought with them.

"It will soon be time for me to go home," Nausicaa told him. "I will show you the way to the city, but you must come in alone. If the princess is seen with a handsome stranger there will be gossip. When you reach the palace, go to my mother and ask for her help."

Later, Odysseus followed the wagon with the maidservants and waited outside the city walls until Nausicaa had disappeared from sight, then he walked through the city gates. He found the palace easily and went through the large golden doors, across a small hall and into the Great Hall itself. A feast was taking place and Odysseus walked directly to the Queen's throne.

"Greetings, my Lady," he said. "I wish you long life and happiness. I've been washed up on your shores, many miles from my home and family, and beg for your help."

King Alcinous waited for the Queen to nod her agreement before ordering food and drink to be brought for Odysseus. "Welcome, stranger," he said. "Come and eat with us."

All through the feast, the Queen watched Odysseus carefully. She had recognised the tunic he was wearing for it was one that she herself had helped to make for one of her sons.

"Where have you come from?" she said to him after the guests were gone and she and the King were alone with Odysseus. "And who gave you that tunic?"

"Good lady, I'm trying to get home, but for seven years I was kept a prisoner on Calypso's island," said Odysseus. "Then I put to sea on a raft which was destroyed in a fierce storm. I was washed up on the Phaeacian shore where your daughter found me, and it was she who gave me the tunic."

"Why did she not bring you here herself?" asked the King.

"She was afraid of gossip, sir," said Odysseus. "But she did everything else in her power to help me, so you must not blame her."

"Ah," said the King, smiling. "You are a thoughtful and sensible man and I would happily let her marry you if you were not so keen to get home. As it is, I'll give you what help I can."

Next day, King Alcinous ordered a ship to be prepared for Odysseus' journey, then invited his strongest oarsmen and all his noblemen to a sporting feast. Demodocus, an old blind minstrel, was also invited and, when the feast began, he began to play his lyre and sing a song. The song was about Troy and Helen, and the great hero Odysseus who had saved her. Odysseus listened sadly, hiding his face so that the others should not see his tears. But King Alcinous noticed his unhappy guest and called everyone out into the courtyard, hoping that the next part of the celebrations would cheer him up.

The young men of Phaeacia wrestled, boxed, threw the discus and javelin, and ran races for the entertainment of Odysseus and the older noblemen. Then King Alcinous' son Laodamus and his friend Euryalus came to see Odysseus.

"Stranger, why not join us in our games?" said Laodamus.

"I'm afraid I can only think about my home," replied Odysseus, "and not about games."

Euryalus scowled. "You are no sporting man," he said. "What are you, a merchant? Someone who thinks only of money and a good bargain?"

This angered Odysseus. He jumped up, took the largest and heaviest discus and threw it farther than any of the Phaeacians had done. "Now!" he said. "Challenge me with wrestling or boxing! Or what about the javelin?"

But no one challenged him.

King Alcinous apologised for Euryalus' rudeness. To the others he said, "When this man leaves our shores, let it be with gifts to remind him of happier moments in Phaeacia." And as the feast continued, Odysseus was brought gifts – cups and bowls made of silver, fine clothes and jewellery. The King and Queen added gifts of their own, and Euryalus – anxious to make amends – gave Odysseus a splendid bronze sword.

Later, Odysseus saw Nausicaa waiting in the shadows and took his chance for a secret word with her. "You saved my life," he told her, "and for that I shall always remember you, even when I am home again."

"I'm glad of that," she replied, and slipped quietly away before he could see her tears.

Odysseus asked Demodocus if he could sing a song about the wooden horse of Troy, and the minstrel sang the story that Odysseus knew so well. Once more, he could not hide his sadness from the King.

"Stranger," said King Alcinous, "will you not tell us your name? From your tears, it would seem you were a warrior at Troy."

"It's true," admitted Odysseus. "I'm Odysseus, King of Ithaca." And he told everyone in the Great Hall of all that had happened to him at Troy and afterwards. He talked and they listened far into the night. Then Odysseus slept.

The ship was loaded with the gifts from the people of Phaeacia and a comfortable bed was put in the bottom of the boat. Carefully, the sleeping Odysseus was lifted down on to the bed and the fifty-two crewmen began to row.

"Goodbye, Odysseus," said King Alcinous. "Sleep well. When you awake, you will be home."

Days and nights passed, but Odysseus slept on. When at last the ship reached Ithaca, the crew lifted him gently on to the shore and surrounded him with the many gifts from the Phaeacians, then they rowed away.

But Poseidon was watching them. He was angry that they had helped Odysseus and, when their ship was within sight of Phaeacia, he raised his mighty trident over them and turned both ship and crew into a huge rock. Forever after, it would be a reminder to the Phaeacians of Poseidon's terrifying power.

Ithaca

Odysseus woke up to find himself surrounded by treasures, but a thick mist hid
most of the land. "Where am I?" he said.

Athene appeared out of the mist, disguised as a
shepherd girl. "This is Ithaca," she said.

Odysseus looked at her closely for he had been
tricked so often. Suddenly, she disappeared – and
a beautiful young woman in a white tunic and
golden helmet stood in her place.

"Do you recognise me, Odysseus?" she said.

"Athene!" he said. "If it really is you, lift this
mist so that I can see where I am."

She smiled and nodded – and suddenly the
mist was gone!

Odysseus looked around, and his heart leapt
for joy! He really was in Ithaca! He saw the
familiar hills and the little harbour.

"Thank you, thank you, Athene!" he cried,
weeping with happiness.

"Yes, you are home, Odysseus," said Athene,
"but there are things you must know. First we

will hide your treasures and make certain that
no one recognises you." And she changed his
appearance so that Odysseus looked like an old
beggar, his clothes rags, his face wrinkled and his
hair grey.

"What is it I must know?" said Odysseus,
suddenly remembering Agamemnon in Hades,
who had returned home only to be killed by his
wife's lover. Did the same fate await him?

"You must visit your old servant, Eumaeus,
who looks after your pigs," said Athene, "and discover what has happened while you have been
away. I must go to Sparta where Telemachus is
about to set sail on a dangerous voyage. An
ambush awaits him, but do not fear, I shall guard
him."

And before Odysseus could ask any questions
about his son, Athene had disappeared. There
was nothing left but to do as she had told him, so
he set off to find his old servant, Eumaeus.

The old man was sitting on the doorstep of his hut as Odysseus approached. Four fierce dogs, who were guarding the pigs, rushed forward when they saw Odysseus. Eumaeus whistled and called them back.

"I'm sorry," the old man said to Odysseus, "but the dogs are only serving my master by protecting his pigs."

"And who is your master?" asked Odysseus.

"King Odysseus," replied Eumaeus. "He was a warrior in the Trojan wars but never returned. He is almost certainly dead. If only he was here now, things would be very different."

"What things?" asked Odysseus.

Eumaeus told him about the suitors who were trying to steal the King's wife. Odysseus listened, his anger growing at every word. Later, the old servant made Odysseus a meal, then gave him a bed to sleep in. It was a wet, wild night and the wind howled around the tiny hut as Odysseus slept and his faithful old servant watched over his pigs.

Meanwhile, in Menelaus' palace, Telemachus was having a dream.

"Take care, Telemachus," Athene was telling him in his dream, "for the suitors have planned an ambush for you at sea. Sail home only in the darkest night and, immediately you come ashore, go quickly to see Eumaeus."

Next morning, Telemachus said goodbye to Menelaus and Helen and set off for Pylos with Peisistratus. They arrived the evening of the following day but Telemachus was so anxious to get back to Ithaca that he asked Peisistratus to say goodbye to King Nestor for him, then hurried to his ship.

The crewmen rowed urgently and they made good time. On the second evening, when they were close to Ithaca, Telemachus ordered his men to stop. "We must wait until it is dark before we go on," he said.

When the night closed over them, the crew began to row again. Not a man spoke. The soft splash of the oars was the only sound in the darkness. Telemachus sat tense and watchful in his seat.

But they had given the suitors the slip by coming in on this side of the island, and at dawn Telemachus ordered his men to drop him at the beach near the hut of Eumaeus, and then to row the ship home. "I'll make the rest of the journey on foot," he told them. "You are safe now."

And he hurried off towards Eumaeus' hut.

Odysseus was talking with Eumaeus when they heard the dogs barking. They looked out and saw the animals running around a young man, jumping up and licking his hands. It was Telemachus, and Odysseus wanted to cry out.

Eumaeus was already greeting Telemachus warmly. "Come in, come in," he said. "We've all been worried for your safety, young master."

Telemachus looked at Odysseus. "Who is this man?"

"He's a wanderer," said Eumaeus. "Last night he told me his story. He fought at Troy with King Odysseus and came to see if his old friend could help him."

Telemachus looked embarrassed. "I wish I could welcome you to my father's house, stranger," he said, "but it is filled with wicked men who would insult you. Stay here with Eumaeus and I'll send food and new clothes for you." He turned to Eumaeus. "Go and tell the Queen I have returned safely, but don't speak to

anyone else. I need time to find out what the suitors plan to do next."

Eumaeus hurried away and, moments later, Athene appeared. Only Odysseus could see her and she signalled to him to come outside.

"The time has come for Telemachus to know who you are," she said, and she touched Odysseus and he was changed back to his real self. "You must work together to get rid of the suitors, and do not be afraid for I'll always be with you."

When Odysseus went back into the hut, Telemachus was astonished by the change. "Who – who are you?" he gasped. "Are you a God?"

"I am your father," said Odysseus.

"I don't believe you!" said Telemachus. "Only a God could be a beggar one moment, and a nobleman the next."

"It was Athene who changed me, my son," Odysseus said quietly.

Telemachus stared at him. "Is – is it really you, Father? Tell me, what's been happening to you?"

"Later," said Odysseus, putting an arm around him. "There are more important things to do first. How many of these suitors are there?"

"There are more than a hundred," said Telemachus. "We cannot – "

"We shall have help," said Odysseus. "Athene will be with us. Now, let's make our plans."

Late that night, Eumaeus returned, but not before Odysseus was changed back to a beggar again.

Eumaeus had bad news for Telemachus. "I told the Queen that you had returned safely," he said, "but I fear that the suitors know it too."

"How?" asked Telemachus.

"Gossip from one of the men on your ship," said Eumaeus. "You will be in danger if you go back to the palace."

"They wouldn't dare harm me there," said Telemachus. "I shall go back early in the morning and you, Eumaeus, must bring our stranger friend in to town later in the morning."

He smiled at Odysseus, and Odysseus smiled back.

In the
Palace

On the afternoon of the following day – many hours after Telemachus had secretly made his way into the palace and met with Penelope – Odysseus and Eumaeus walked towards the town. Melanthius, a herdsman, saw them coming. He was driving some of Odysseus' cattle to the palace for the suitors.

"Where are you taking that beggar, Eumaeus?" he said. "We don't want beggars in the palace." And he kicked Odysseus.

"One day soon, you will pay for that," said Odysseus.

"You should be ashamed!" Eumaeus told Melanthius. "If King Odysseus was at the palace, he would make all men welcome."

"Your master is dead," said Melanthius. "I only wish his son was dead, too."

Odysseus and Eumaeus followed the herdsmen to the town. In the palace courtyard, Odysseus noticed a dog lying on the ground. It was Argus, his old hunting dog, but the animal was too weak to move. Odysseus bent down to stroke his dog and it lifted its head, recognising his master's touch. The dog tried to stand up, but it was too much for him.

Odysseus walked on with tears in his eyes and, with a last look at its master, the old dog died peacefully.

Once inside the Great Hall, Odysseus saw Telemachus with the suitors. They were pre-tending to be friendly with the young prince but Odysseus knew it was all make-believe. At the first opportunity, the suitors would carry out their plan to murder Telemachus.

When the suitors saw the beggar, most of them gave him something from their plate. But Antinous gave him nothing.

"We have enough beggars in Ithaca," he said. "Why have you brought us another, Eumaeus?"

Odysseus stood close to Antinous. "I was a rich man before my luck changed," he said. "Now I depend on the kindness of men like you."

"I don't want to hear your tale of woe," said Antinous. "Go away." And he snatched up a stool and threw it at the beggar.

Odysseus took the blow without moving, although Telemachus almost cried out as he saw the treatment his father was receiving. Then Odysseus sat down, outwardly calm but burning with anger inside.

Suddenly, another beggar came into the Great Hall. It was Irus, a lazy and very greedy man who preferred to beg rather than work.

"Go away!" he said when he saw Odysseus. "This is my place to beg."

"There is enough for both of us," Odysseus told him.

Irus showed Odysseus his fist. "Go now, or you'll regret it."

Antinous heard him and laughed. "Look!" he

shouted. "We are about to be entertained with a fight!"

Odysseus tucked in his tunic at the waist and took off his ragged cloak. There was surprised whispering among the suitors when they saw the muscles on his arms and legs. Irus saw them too, and his appetite for a fight disappeared. He tried to slip away but was pushed back.

Each man put up his fists and began to move around the other, Irus trying to stay out of harm's way. Then Odysseus came closer and Irus struck out wildly, catching Odysseus on the shoulder. Odysseus struck back with a blow to Irus' chin – and Irus fell to the ground with a thud.

The suitors laughed and raised their wine glasses as Odysseus dragged the poor Irus from the hall and into the courtyard. When he returned, the suitors cheered and clapped and gave him wine to drink and food to eat from the table.

As all these things happened, Penelope slept. Now she woke and, looking as lovely as a young bride (for Athene had been at work), she came downstairs to the Great Hall. A silence fell over the room and there were gasps of admiration at her beauty. Odysseus wanted to run and put his arms around her, but dared not.

"My beloved Odysseus has not returned and is almost certainly dead," said Penelope, looking beautiful but very sad. "And my son is now a man. Therefore, the time has come when I must choose another husband."

The suitors became excited as they heard this.

"Choose the best of us!" called Antinous.

"It is the custom for suitors to bring presents," Penelope reminded them. "Then perhaps tomorrow I can decide."

So each of the suitors sent a servant to bring some of their treasures for Penelope. The servants returned with jewellery and precious stones and took them to Penelope's room, and the Queen followed.

The suitors immediately began to celebrate, each imagining they would be the fortunate one to be chosen. Much wine was drunk that night, and there was laughter and singing. Some of the servant girls joined in and Odysseus watched them angrily.

'Why do they not think about their unhappy mistress instead of making merry with these wicked men?' he thought.

When he said this to them, they laughed at him.

"Go away, you silly old man!" they said.

Telemachus shouted above the noise. "Enough! It's time you all went to your beds!"

The suitors were surprised at his boldness but did as they were told.

When Telemachus and Odysseus were alone they quickly took the swords, shields, spears and

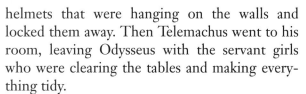

helmets that were hanging on the walls and locked them away. Then Telemachus went to his room, leaving Odysseus with the servant girls who were clearing the tables and making everything tidy.

"Are you still here, old beggar?" they said.

"Be careful," said Odysseus. "You, too, may be unlucky soon."

At that moment, Penelope came into the room. She had heard the servants' unkind words and ordered them to put a chair on the other side of the large fireplace, opposite hers. "Now go away," she said. "I want to speak with this man."

Odysseus waited as Penelope sat down, then settled himself in the chair beside her. "How can I help you?" he asked.

"Eumaeus says you may have news of Odysseus," she said. "If only you could tell me he was alive and coming home, then I would not have to take another husband."

"I first met your husband when he was on his way to Troy, twenty years ago," said Odysseus. "He was a good man."

Penelope was cautious for she had been deceived before. "What was he wearing?" she asked.

"A crimson cloak, fastened at the shoulder with a golden brooch," said Odysseus. "The brooch was most unusual. Half was shaped like a dog, and the other half was shaped like the deer that the dog was hunting."

Tears filled Penelope's eyes. "Those are the clothes I gave him, and the brooch was my own favourite. But what else do you know of him?"

"I have heard that he angered Zeus, who wrecked his ship and drowned his men," said Odysseus. "But they say Odysseus escaped, and that he will return home very soon, in disguise. Believe me, he is close to you now."

"I wish I could believe you, stranger," said Penelope, with a sigh. "I will send Eurycleia to you. She was nurse to Telemachus, and was once nurse to Odysseus himself. She will bathe your tired feet before you go to bed."

"Thank you," said Odysseus, smiling to him-self as he remembered the old nurse.

Eurycleia came with a basin of warm water and Odysseus tucked up his tunic in readiness. He was about to place his feet in the warm water when Eurycleia's hands flew to her face, knocking over the basin, and she gave a gasp. Odysseus realised at once what had happened. His old nurse had seen a scar on his leg – the result of a tussle with a boar when he had been hunting one day as a young man – and had recognised it.

"Shh!" Odysseus whispered to her. "Say nothing to anyone! No one must know I'm here until those suitors are gone."

Eurycleia's face was filled with joy. "I will keep silent," she whispered, excitedly.

Penelope had heard nothing. She was staring into the fire, her thoughts far away. But then she said, "The other night I dreamed that an eagle killed all twenty of my pet geese, then spoke to me with the voice of Odysseus. It said, 'Do not cry, Penelope, for as the eagle has killed the geese, so will I kill the suitors.'"

"The eagle is Zeus's bird," said Odysseus. "It is a good omen."

Penelope sighed. "I hope you're right. But I still have one more trick to play on the suitors tomorrow."

After this, Penelope went to her room and Odysseus was left alone in the Great Hall where a bed had been made up for him. But sleep did not come easily. For many hours he lay awake, his mind busy with his plans for the next day.

The Great Bow

Penelope awoke to the sound of thunder. She dressed quickly then hurried to a secret room and unlocked the door. Inside, on the wall, was a huge bow and a quiver full of arrows. They belonged to Odysseus. Penelope took them off the wall and carried them back to her room.

Downstairs everyone was getting ready for a feast in honour of the God Apollo. Odysseus watched all the activity as the Great Hall filled with people. The suitors whispered together and Telemachus kept himself busy making sure everything was in order.

Eumaeus arrived with another herdsman, Philoetius, who asked who the beggar was. "His noble face reminds me of our master, Odysseus," said Philoetius. "Oh, how I wish Odysseus was here now so that I could stand with him against these terrible men!"

"I, too," agreed Eumaeus.

Odysseus heard these words and would remember them later.

The feast began and the suitors filled their plates. Most of them ignored Odysseus but one of them, Ctesippus, laughed and said, "The beggar deserves an extra portion of meat!" And he threw a large bone at Odysseus. Odysseus moved quickly and it hit the wall.

"Stop that!" cried Telemachus. "I've seen enough of your cowardly attacks on an old man. One more and you'll have me to answer to!"

The suitors fell silent, and a wise old man spoke to them.

"You are fools," he told them. "I can see much blood, and a hundred spirits on their way to Hades! None of you will escape!" And he turned and walked from the room as the suitors laughed nervously.

Penelope made her entrance just moments after the wise man had left. She was carrying the great bow and the quiver of arrows. Behind her were servants carrying twelve axe heads, each axe with a bronze loop behind the head.

"What's this?" said Antinous, as Telemachus hammered the axes into the ground in a straight line. "A new game?"

"It's my way of choosing which of you to marry," Penelope told him. "Odysseus was a fine marksman who could shoot an arrow through each of the twelve loops. I will marry the man who can bend the bow and fit its bowstring, and who can fire an arrow through all twelve loops."

Odysseus hid a smile as Eumaeus placed the bow in front of the suitors.

Antinous looked at it. "It will be difficult even to string it," he said. "I remember seeing Odysseus do it when I was a child, but he was very strong."

"Let me try," said Telemachus. But four times he tried and failed.

Then the first of the suitors stepped forward and tried his strength, but it was too much for him, too.

Antinous told Melanthius the herdsman to melt some wax to grease the bow, hoping to make it more supple. But even then no suitor could string it. Now it was Antinous' turn, and as

he struggled with the great weapon, Odysseus moved out to the courtyard to speak with Eumaeus and Philoetius.

"If Odysseus returned, would you fight beside him?" he whispered.

"We would indeed!" they answered together. "He is our King!"

"You are good and loyal men," said Odysseus, "and you will be rewarded – for your King stands before you now!"

And Odysseus lifted his tunic so that the herdsmen could see the hunting scar on his leg. Both men recognised the scar and gasped.

"Odysseus!" Eumaeus cried joyfully.

Both men shook Odysseus' hand and embraced him.

"Listen carefully, Eumaeus," said Odysseus. "I'm going to ask the suitors to let me try my skill with the bow. If they refuse, I want you to bring it to me then bolt all the doors to the hall from the outside."

Back inside the Great Hall, Antinous had failed to string the bow.

"We will try again tomorrow," he said. "This is Apollo's feast day, and no fit time for such a contest."

"I would like to try," said Odysseus, stepping forward.

But Antinous was taking no risks after seeing the beggar's fight with Irus. "Are you still here?" he said. "Go away and don't interfere."

"Let him try," said Penelope. "He doesn't intend to claim my hand in marriage, so you've nothing to fear."

Telemachus sensed that something was about to happen. "Mother, it's time to go to your room and rest," he said. "Take the other women with you."

Penelope sighed. "Very well," she said.

As the women left and the suitors were trying to decide what to do, Eumaeus quickly took the bow and gave it to Odysseus. Then he went with Philoetius to bolt the doors.

Without rising from the chair where he was sitting, Odysseus looked carefully at the bow,

bent it, then notched the string at the other end. Still sitting, he pulled an arrow from the quiver and fitted it into place. He took aim – and fired!

Thunder boomed over the palace as the arrow flew through all twelve loops of the axe heads before thudding into the wall. A gasp of astonishment echoed around the room.

Odysseus smiled. "Now it's time for more feasting," he said, still holding the bow. "Let's all be merry."

He gave a small nod to Telemachus who, recognising the signal, grasped his sword, took his spear and went to stand beside his father.

The time had come.

The End of the Odyssey

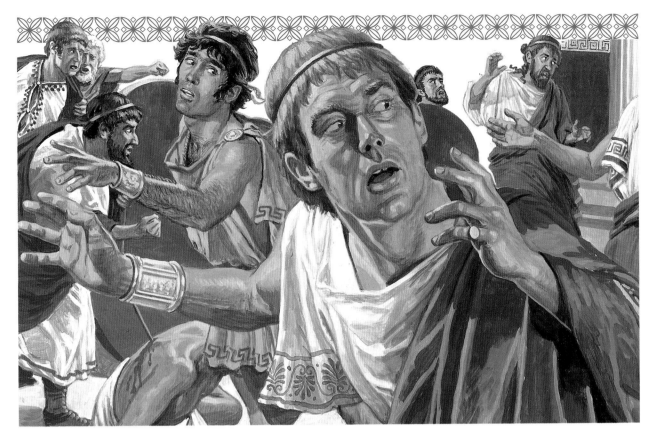

Antinous, raising his cup to his lips, looked puzzled as the beggar lifted an arrow to the bow and took aim once more. Puzzlement turned to horror as he realised the arrow was pointing at him! He opened his mouth to speak, but the arrow struck him in the throat before he could utter a word. The cup slipped from his hand and his legs buckled under him.

The heads of all the suitors turned towards Odysseus. There were angry shouts of "Murderer!" and "You'll pay for that with your life!" before Odysseus shouted them down.

"Do you *still* not know who I am?" he cried. "You, who tried to steal my wife!"

And then they knew.

Faces turned white as they backed away towards the doors. Odysseus was already fitting another arrow into the great bow. The suitors looked for the spears and swords which usually hung on the walls but saw only blank spaces. They tried to escape through the doors but found them bolted. There was nothing left but to face Odysseus and Telemachus.

Eurymachus drew his sword and ran forward –

only to be struck down by Odysseus' second arrow. Another man tried his luck, but Telemachus' spear thumped into his chest before he had gone more than a few paces. Then Odysseus started firing arrows in all directions as Telemachus ran for more weapons. Men fell to the ground before they could hide, and Eumaeus and Philoetius joined Odysseus, already armed with spears.

Telemachus came back with spears and shields but Melanthius had seen where the weapons were hidden and hurried to find weapons for the remaining suitors. He succeeded once, bringing spears and shields for the suitors, but when he tried a second time, Eumaeus and Philoetius caught him and tied him to a pillar with rope.

They went back to join Odysseus and Telemachus and the four of them faced the onslaught from the rest of the suitors. Six spears flew at Odysseus but Athene was watching over him and changed their direction so that they went harmlessly into doorposts or walls. Then Odysseus and his companions brought down four men with their spears and, as the others retreated, rescued their weapons and threw again. Ctesippus, who had insulted Odysseus, took the full force of Philoetius' spear whilst other suitors died by the sword.

Melanthius was cut free and was then killed, as were all the servants who had been disloyal to Odysseus and Penelope. Only when the blood and bodies had been cleared away did Odysseus send Eurycleia to fetch Queen Penelope from her room.

When Penelope was told that her husband was home, and that he had killed all the suitors, she could not believe it.

"It is true!" Eurycleia insisted.

Penelope was full of doubts. She dressed and came down to the Great Hall where she saw Telemachus standing with another man in the shadows beside the fireplace. Penelope could find no words to say. Was it really Odysseus? she wondered.

"Mother," said Telemachus, "have you nothing to say to your husband after all these years?"

"How do I know it's him?" said Penelope.

Then Athene changed Odysseus' appearance

from beggar to King. The rags disappeared and a splendid tunic with a gold belt and purple cloak took their place.

Penelope saw the man she loved, but even then she hesitated. She turned to Eurycleia. "This man may sleep in Odysseus' bed tonight," she said, an idea forming in her mind. "Have it moved from my bedroom."

Odysseus laughed. "That's impossible. I built that bed myself, around a living olive tree. No one can move it without cutting down the head-post which was once the olive tree!"

When Penelope heard this she knew it really was Odysseus before her. No one else could have known about the bed. She ran into his arms weeping with joy, and he held her close, his tears mingling with hers.

Next day, Odysseus went with Telemachus, Eumaeus and Philoetius to find Laertes. Odysseus' father was working at the farm where he had lived for many years, broken-hearted because of the loss of his son. At first he did not recognise Odysseus.

"Who is this stranger?" Laertes asked Telemachus.

"Look again, Grandfather," said Telemachus. "It's no stranger."

The old man looked at Odysseus more closely – and the shock was almost too much for him. "Odysseus!" he cried. "My son!" And the two men embraced warmly, unable to find words to say.

But before they finished greeting one another, Telemachus cried out a warning. "Look! We have visitors, and they do not look friendly!"

Odysseus moved away from his father and looked across the hills where he saw a group of men hurrying towards the farm. At the head of them was Eupeithes, the father of Antinous.

Odysseus and his companions stood with spears at the ready as the men approached. But before Eupeithes and the others could use their own weapons, Athene appeared between the two groups.

"Stop!" she cried. "There has been enough killing, Eupeithes. The suitors were punished by the Gods for their evil deeds. Odysseus only carried out that punishment. Now, let there be peace."

A thunderbolt from Zeus emphasized these words, and the Ithacan men put down their weapons, ready to talk peace.

And so the Odyssey ended.

There was a great feast for all the people of Ithaca to celebrate the return of King Odysseus, and the merry-making went on late into the night in that happy land. Odysseus was home!